Black Girl Shine Books Presents

BLACK BOY
WE NEED YOU

Individual

Creative

Influential

Hardworking

Happy

By Shavondra Walker

Illustrated by AM Studio
Editor Renea Walker

Dedication
for the Culture

To Black Boys Everywhere continue to be better than the rest!

We love You!

BLACK BOY WE NEED YOU TO BE

ONE OF A KIND

You are the top scholar in your class.

You are handsome.

You are the dreamer
that makes
his dreams come true.

You are royal, embrace your crown.

Treat yourself and others with kindness and respect.

It is okay to cry.

BLACK BOY

WE NEED YOU TO BE

CREATIVE

Be the talented artist that paints beautiful masterpieces.

Be the Musician that creates music to move the people.

Be the next
best-selling Author.

Be the Leader that helps your community.

Be the Educator that teaches our youth.

Be the scientist that cures diseases.

Be the Athlete that sets records.

Be the firefighter that saves lives.

Be the Solider that fights for his country.

Be the Mechanic that repairs cars.

Be the Chef that cooks delicious meals.

Be the TRUSTING Police Officer that PROTECTS and SERVES his community.

Be the next entrepreneur that opens a business in your community.

Be the barber that cuts hair on Saturday mornings.

Be the truck driver that travels across the country to deliver cargo.

BLACK BOY
WE NEED YOU TO BE
HAPPY

I am loved and appreciated.

I love to laugh and smile until my cheeks hurt.

I am NOT BAD and I MATTER.

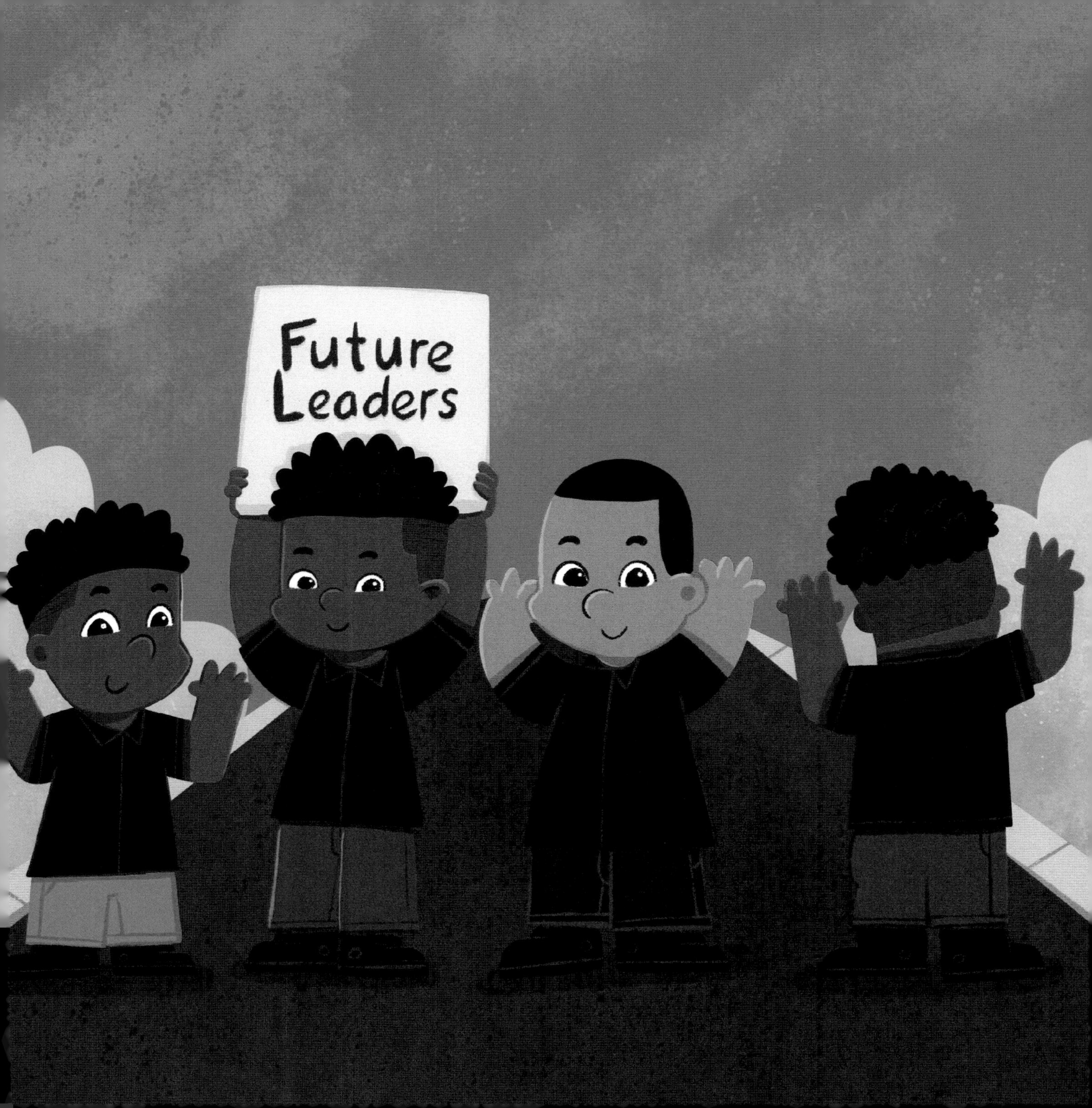
Future
Leaders

BLACK BOY WE NEED YOU TO BE

THE BEST

SMART

HAPPY

FUNNY

BLACK BOY WE NEED YOU TO BE

HONEST

CREATIVE

CONFIDENT

A LEADER

Hello from the Author!

Shavondra Walker is an HBCU graduate from Chicago, IL with an undeniable passion for uplifting and empowering the Black Community.

Shavondra arrived on the writing scene in 2018 with the award-winning affirmation-based children's books "Black Girl Shine". She takes pride in pouring positivity into our children.

Shavondra is back with Black Boy We Need You and eager to encourage and empower our boys.

Shavondra enjoys speaking to the youth and elevating the community.
She aspires to inspire children all over the world to be confident in who they are and their ability to succeed, with that the possibilities are endless!

Contact the Author
Email:Blackgirlshinebooks@gmail.com
Website:Blackgirlshinebooks.com
Facebook: Blackgirlshinebooks
Instagram: Blackgirlshinebooks

Thank You from the Author

Thank you to the readers that will be inspired by the Black Girl Shine book brand.
I would like to thank my family and friends for continuing to
push me beyond limitations and providing unlimited love and support.
The Black Girl Shine Books team is amazing. I am forever grateful. Thank You.